Contents

Step I: Two-digit subtraction no exchange

When learning written subtraction, it is important to know how to set numbers out vertically with the correct digits in the correct columns. Here, 87 and 36 are correctly written under the Tens and Units headings.

What to do

87 − 36 = ?

	T	U
	8	7
−	3	6

I   Set out the numbers in the correct columns with one digit in each square.

2   Always start at the right-hand side, with the units column! Subtract the bottom digit from the top digit. 7 − 6 = 1

	T	U
	8	7
−	3	6
		1

3   Next move to the left and look at the digits in the tens column. Subtract the bottom digit from the top digit. 8 − 3 = 5

4   Finally, look at the answer and check whether it seems a sensible answer. You can add the answer to the number subtracted to see if it gives you the top number. 51 + 36 = 87 Yes, this is correct.

	T	U
	8	7
−	3	6
	5	1

Now you try

I   96 − 44 = ?

	T	U
	9	6
−	4	4
		2

2   75 − 31 = ?

	T	U
	7	5
−	3	1
		4

3   68 − 42 = ?

	T	U
	6	8
−	4	2

4   58 − 27 = ?

	T	U
	5	8
−	2	7

5   87 − 24 = ?

	T	U
	8	7
−	2	4

6   79 − 46 = ?

	T	U
	7	9
−	4	6

More practice   Set out these questions yourself to answer them.

7 78 – 24 = ?

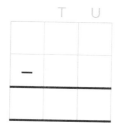

8 95 – 33 = ?

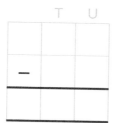

9 88 – 46 = ?

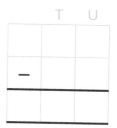

10 Check your answers above by adding.

54 + 24 =

Problem solving

11 A shop had a shelf with 89 tins on it.
If 43 of the tins are bought, how many
tins remain on the shelf?

12 Mrs Smith only has 78p in her purse.
She takes out 45p to pay in a car park.
How much money is left in the purse?

13 The height of Jo's dog is 93cm. The height
of Jo's cat is 23cm. How much taller is Jo's
dog than Jo's cat?

14 David weighed 86kg before going on
a diet. After his diet he weighs 72kg.
How many kilograms did he lose?

How did I find Step 1?   ☐ Easy   ☐ OK   ☐ Difficult

Step 2: Three-digit subtraction no exchange

For three-digit numbers, work in the same way. Make sure the numbers are set out in the correct columns in the same way. Here, 576 and 143 are correctly written under the Hundreds, Tens and Units headings.

What to do

$576 - 143 = ?$

	H	T	U
	5	7	6
−	1	4	3

1 Set out the numbers in the correct columns with one digit in each square.

	H	T	U
	5	7	6
−	1	4	3
			3

2 Always start at the right-hand side, with the units column! Subtract the bottom digit from the top digit. $6 - 3 = 3$

	H	T	U
	5	7	6
−	1	4	3
		3	3

3 Next, move to the left and look at the digits in the tens column. Subtract the bottom digit from the top digit. $7 - 4 = 3$

	H	T	U
	5	7	6
−	1	4	3
	4	3	3

4 Then move to the left again and subtract the bottom digit from the top digit in the hundreds column. $5 - 1 = 4$

5 Finally, look at the answer and check whether it seems a sensible answer. $433 + 143$ is 576, which is correct!

Now you try

1 $489 - 144 = ?$

	H	T	U
	4	8	9
−	1	4	4
			5

2 $575 - 214 = ?$

	H	T	U
	5	7	5
−	2	1	4
			1

3 $859 - 435 = ?$

	H	T	U
	8	5	9
−	4	3	5
			4

4 $583 - 271 = ?$

	H	T	U
	5	8	3
−	2	7	1

5 $837 - 224 = ?$

	H	T	U
	8	3	7
−	2	2	4

6 $794 - 464 = ?$

	H	T	U
	7	9	4
−	4	6	4

More practice

Set out these questions yourself to answer them.

7 475 − 123 = ?

```
  H   T   U
┌───┬───┬───┐
│   │   │   │
├───┼───┼───┤
│ ─ │   │   │
└───┴───┴───┘
```

8 888 − 447 = ?

```
  H   T   U
┌───┬───┬───┐
│   │   │   │
├───┼───┼───┤
│ ─ │   │   │
└───┴───┴───┘
```

9 739 − 127 = ?

```
  H   T   U
┌───┬───┬───┐
│   │   │   │
├───┼───┼───┤
│ ─ │   │   │
└───┴───┴───┘
```

10 967 − 264 = ?

```
  H   T   U
┌───┬───┬───┐
│   │   │   │
├───┼───┼───┤
│ ─ │   │   │
└───┴───┴───┘
```

11 469 − 327 = ?

```
  H   T   U
┌───┬───┬───┐
│   │   │   │
├───┼───┼───┤
│ ─ │   │   │
└───┴───┴───┘
```

12 573 − 402 = ?

```
  H   T   U
┌───┬───┬───┐
│   │   │   │
├───┼───┼───┤
│ ─ │   │   │
└───┴───┴───┘
```

Problem solving

13 A farmer had 678 sheep. She sells 315 of them at market. How many sheep has she now?

_____

14 Kim had £468 in a bank account. She took out £225. How much money stayed in the bank account?

_____

15 Two numbers have a difference of 733. If the larger number is 969, what is the smaller number?

_____

16 687 people went to a football match. 136 of them left early. How many people were there at the end?

_____

How did I find Step 2? ☐ Easy ☐ OK ☐ Difficult

Step 3: Three-digit subtraction exchanging
1 ten for 10 units

These questions have one digit in the bottom number that is larger than the digit above it.

See here that the 8 is larger than the 3 above it!

	H	T	U
	5	7	3
−	1	4	8

What to do

1 You can't take 8 away from 3 so you must exchange ten from the column to its left. Cross out the 7 tens and write one fewer above it. One fewer than 7 is 6.

2 Now, take the ten you have exchanged and write it in the units column, so instead of 3 units you now have 10 + 3 = 13. Now you can take away 8 from 13 and get the answer 5.

3 Then complete the rest of the subtraction as normal, working from right to left.

573 − 148 = ?

	H	T	U
			6
	5	~~7~~	3
−	1	4	8

	H	T	U
			6
	5	~~7~~	¹3
−	1	4	8
			5

	H	T	U
			6
	5	~~7~~	¹3
−	1	4	8
	4	2	5

Now you try

1

		6	
	4	~~7~~	¹3
−	1	3	8
			5

2

		8	
	7	9	3
−	2	3	6

3

		4	
	8	5	2
−	4	1	5

4

		7	
	7	8	4
−	2	5	7

5

	6	5	3
−	2	1	9

6

	4	8	2
−	1	6	7

7

	8	~~7~~	6
−	5	5	7

8

	9	3	4
−	6	1	9

9

	8	8	1
−	7	2	7

More practice

10

```
   4 7 5
 - 1 4 7
 _____
```

11

```
   5 9 3
 - 2 8 6
 _____
```

12

```
   6 2 4
 - 4 1 8
 _____
```

Set out these questions yourself to answer them.

13 475 – 128 = ?

H   T   U

14 886 – 447 = ?

H   T   U

15 730 – 127 = ?

H   T   U

16 967 – 259 = ?

H   T   U

17 465 – 327 = ?

H   T   U

18 573 – 406 = ?

H   T   U

Problem solving

19 Subtract 327 from 574.

_____

20 Joe had £465 in a bank account. He took out £228. How much money was left in the bank account?

_____

| How did I find Step 3? | ☐ Easy | ☐ OK | ☐ Difficult |

Step 4: Three-digit subtraction exchanging 1 hundred for 10 tens

	H	T	U
	5	3	6
−	1	8	5

As for Step 3, these questions have one digit in the bottom number that is larger than the digit above it, but this time it is the tens digit.

See here that the 8 is larger than the 3 above it! ⟶

What to do

$536 − 185 = ?$

	H	T	U
	5	3	6
−	1	8	5
			1

1 Start with the units. Subtract 5 from 6 leaving 1.

2 Then move left to the tens. Because you can't take 8 away from 3, you must exchange one hundred from the column to its left. Cross out the 5 hundreds and write one fewer above it. One fewer than 5 is 4.

3 Next take the hundred you have exchanged and write it in the tens column, so instead of 3 tens you now have 10 tens + 3 tens = 13 tens. Now you can take away 8 from 13 to get 5.

	⁴		
	5̶	¹3	6
−	1	8	5
		5	1

4 Finally, look at the hundreds column. Subtract 1 hundred from the 4 hundreds that are left to give 3 hundreds.

	⁴		
	5̶	¹3	6
−	1	8	5
	3	5	1

Now you try

1

	⁴		
	5̶	¹2	3
−	1	4	2
			1

2

	⁶		
	7̶	¹4	8
−	2	7	6
			2

3

	⁷		
	8̶	¹3	9
−	4	9	5
			4

4

	⁶		
	7̶	5	4
−	2	8	2

5

	6	5	6
−	2	8	6

6

	4	6	8
−	1	7	7

More practice

7
```
    4  0  9
 -  1  4  7
 _____

 _____
```

8
```
    8  1  8
 -  2  8  6
 _____

 _____
```

9
```
    6  4  9
 -  4  6  8
 _____

 _____
```

Set out these questions yourself to answer them.

10 477 − 193 = ?

H   T   U

11 826 − 474 = ?

H   T   U

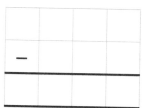

12 736 − 186 = ?

H   T   U

13 967 − 283 = ?

H   T   U

14 415 − 321 = ?

H   T   U

15 543 − 452 = ?

H   T   U

Problem solving

16 Use subtraction to find the difference between 547 and 175.

17 A safari park has 636 animals. If 184 of them are monkeys, how many of the animals are not monkeys?

| **How did I find Step 4?** | ☐ Easy | ☐ OK | ☐ Difficult |

Step 5: Three-digit subtraction exchanging once

On these pages, you must decide when to exchange. Sometimes you will need to exchange a ten and sometimes you will need to exchange a hundred. Look for when a digit in the bottom number is larger than the digit above it.

What to do

773 – 255 = ?

	H	T	U
		6	
	7	8̶	¹3
–	2	5	5

1 Start with the units. Is the bottom digit larger than the top digit? Is 5 larger than 3? Yes. So you must exchange a ten.

2 If the lower digit is larger you must exchange one from the column to its left. Here, exchange 1 ten. Cross out the 7 tens and write one fewer above it. One fewer than 7 is 6.

		6	
	7	8̶	¹3
–	2	5	5
			8

3 Next, take the ten you have exchanged and write it in the units column, so instead of 3 units you now have 10 + 3 = 13 units.

4 Now you can take away 5 from 13 to get 8.

5 Continue with the subtraction in the same way, working from right to left.

		6	
	7	8̶	¹3
–	2	5	5
	5	1	8

Now you try

1

		7	
	8	¹1	5
–	1	4	2
			3

2

		3	
	6	4̶	¹3
–	2	2	6

3

		7	
	8	¹3	6
–	2	6	5

4

	7	5	5
–	2	9	2

5

	6	6	6
–	2	5	8

6

	4	4	8
–	1	2	9

More practice

7
```
    4  0  8
 -  2  5  3
_____
```

8
```
    8  9  1
 -  2  8  6
_____
```

9
```
    8  4  5
 -  7  8  3
_____
```

Set out these questions yourself to answer them.

10 592 − 245 = ?

11 746 − 284 = ?

12 736 − 685 = ?

13 925 − 317 = ?

14 885 − 306 = ?

15 537 − 252 = ?

Problem solving

16 A plane has 697 passengers. If 348 of them are male, how many are female?

_____

17 A skyscraper is 243m tall. It stands next to a cathedral that is 171m tall. How much taller is the skyscraper than the cathedral?

_____

| **How did I find Step 5?** | ☐ Easy | ☐ OK | ☐ Difficult |

Check-up test 1 Two- and three-digit subtraction, including one exchange

Step 1

1   79 – 46 = ?

```
    7  9
 -  4  6
```

2   57 – 23 = ?

```
    5  7
 -  2  3
```

3   89 – 24 = ?

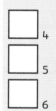

Step 2

4   593 – 251 = ?

```
    5  9  3
 -  2  5  1
```

5   737 – 234 = ?

```
    7  3  7
 -  2  3  4
```

6   794 – 464 = ?

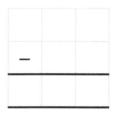

Step 3

7   934 – 518 = ?

```
    9  3  4
 -  5  1  8
```

8   771 – 147 = ?

```
    7  7  1
 -  1  4  7
```

9   876 – 128 = ?

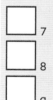

Step 4

10   468 – 174 = ?

```
    4  6  8
 -  1  7  4
```

11   649 – 468 = ?

```
    6  4  9
 -  4  6  8
```

12   614 – 521 = ?

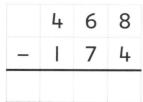

Step 5

13 692 – 245 = ?   **14** 726 – 683 = ?   **15** 706 – 385 = ?

☐ 13

☐ 14

☐ 15

Steps 1 to 5 mixed

Use the grid below for working.

16 Find the difference between 356 and 588.   _____   ☐ 16

17 A farmer had 693 cows. He sells 374 of them.
How many cows has he now?   _____   ☐ 17

18 Subtract 281 from 457.   _____   ☐ 18

19 Find the difference between 953 and 272.   _____   ☐ 19

Total test score

Score	1	2	3	4	5	6	7	8	9	10	11	12	13	14	15	16	17	18	19
%	5	11	16	21	26	32	37	42	47	53	58	63	68	74	79	84	89	95	100

_____
19

Step 6: Four-digit subtraction exchanging 1 thousand for 10 hundreds

As for previous steps, these questions have one digit in the bottom number that is larger than the digit above it, but this time it is the hundreds digit.

See here that the 8 is larger than the 1 above it. ⟶

Th	H	T	U
	6	1	8	7
–	1	8	2	3

What to do

$6187 - 1823 = ?$

1   Start with the units. $7 - 3 = 4$

2   Move left to the tens. $8 - 2 = 6$

Th	H	T	U
	6	1	8	7
–	1	8	2	3
			6	4

3   Then move to the hundreds. Because you can't take 8 away from 1, you must exchange 1 thousand from the column to its left. Cross out the 6 thousands and write one fewer above it. One fewer than 6 is 5.

	5			
	6̶	1	8	7
–	1	8	2	3
			6	4

4   Next, take the thousand you have exchanged and write it in the hundreds column, so instead of 1 hundred you now have 10 hundreds + 1 hundred = 11 hundreds.

	5			
	6̶	¹1	8	7
–	1	8	2	3
			3	6	4

5   Now, you can take away 8 from 11 to get 3.

6   Finally, look at the thousands column. Subtract 1 thousand from the 5 thousands that are left to give 4 thousands.

	5			
	6̶	¹1	8	7
–	1	8	2	3
	4	3	6	4

Now you try

1

	7			
	8̶	¹3	6	8
–	4	9	4	2
			2	6

2

	3			
	4̶	5	9	7
–	1	8	1	2
			8	5

3

	6̶	4	8	4
–	5	9	8	3
			0	1

4

	7	2	5	4
–	3	3	2	4
				0

More practice

Set out these questions yourself to answer them.

5 7598 – 2644 = ?

6 8036 – 4514 = ?

7 6483 – 5873 = ?

8 9585 – 6664 = ?

Problem solving

9 Kim had £6747 in a bank account.
She took out £1835 to buy a car.
How much money is left in the account?

10 A car park has 6479 parking spaces.
If 5644 are empty, how many are filled?

| How did I find Step 6? | ☐ Easy | ☐ OK | ☐ Difficult |

Step 7: Four-digit subtraction exchanging a ten and a thousand

For the questions in this step, you will need to exchange twice. In both the units and hundreds columns, the digit in the bottom number is larger than the digit above it. Here, 9 is larger than the 4 above it and 5 is larger than the 1 above it.

Th	H	T	U
	6	1	8	4
−	1	5	3	9

What to do

$6184 - 1539 = ?$

Th	H	T	U
	6	1	8	¹4
−	1	5	3	9
			4	5

1 Start with the units. 9 is larger than 4 so exchange from the tens. Cross out the 8 and write one fewer above it. One fewer than 8 is 7. Next, take the ten you exchanged and write it in the units column, so instead of 4 you now have $10 + 4 = 14$ units. Then subtract. $14 - 9 = 5$

2 Move left to the tens. $7 - 3 = 4$

Th	H	T	U
	⁵6̸	¹1	8̸	¹4
−	1	5	3	9
		6	4	5

3 Then move to the hundreds. Because you can't take 5 away from 1, exchange 1 thousand. Cross out the 6 thousands and write one fewer above it. One fewer than 6 is 5. Take the thousand and write it in the hundreds column, so instead of 1 hundred you now have 10 hundreds + 1 hundred = 11 hundreds. $11 - 5 = 6$

4 Finally, look at the thousands column. Subtract 1 thousand from the 5 thousands that are left to give 4 thousands.

Th	H	T	U
	⁵6̸	¹1	8̸	¹4
−	1	5	3	9
	4	6	4	5

Now you try

1

		8	3	⁵6̸	¹0
−		4	9	4	5
					5

2

		4	5	³4̸	¹7
−		1	8	1	8

3

		9	4	8̸	4
−		5	9	7	7

4

		7	2	5̸	2
−		6	3	2	9

More practice

5
```
    7  5  8  0
 -  6  9  3  8
 _____
```

6
```
    6  3  1  2
 -  2  6  0  4
 _____
```

Set out these questions yourself to answer them.

7 8272 – 4756 = ?

8 9190 – 7614 = ?

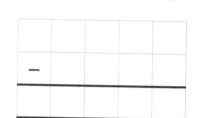

Problem solving

9 Paul's income last year was £8265. This year it was £9171. How much more did he earn this year?

10 A traffic survey counted 4729 vehicles driving west and 6295 driving east along a road. How many more were driving east than west?

11 Sales of the music track 'School Rocks' fell from 8173 last week to 4238 this week. How many fewer is that?

How did I find Step 7?   ☐ Easy   ☐ OK   ☐ Difficult

Step 8: Three-digit subtraction exchanging twice, adjacent digits

	H	T	U
	5	3	4
−	1	7	8

Sometimes, when you need to exchange twice, the two columns are next to each other. Here, the digit in the bottom number is larger than the digit above it in both the units and the tens columns.

What to do

534 − 178 = ?

1 You can't take 8 away from 4 so you must exchange ten from the column to its left. Cross out the 3 tens and write one fewer above it. One fewer than 3 is 2. Take the ten exchanged and write it in the units column, so instead of 4 units you now have 10 + 4 = 14. Now subtract. 14 − 8 = 6

	H	T(2)	U
	5	3̶	¹4
−	1	7	8
			6

2 Now, move to the tens column. 7 is larger than the 2 above it so you need to exchange a hundred from the column to the left. Cross out the 5 hundreds and write one fewer above it. One fewer than 5 is 4. Think of the hundred exchanged as 10 tens and add it to the number of tens. 10 tens + 2 tens = 12 tens. 12 − 7 = 5

	H(4)	T(12)	U
	5̶	3̶	¹4
−	1	7	8
		5	6

3 Then complete the rest of the subtraction as normal, working from right to left. 4 − 1 = 3

	H(4)	T(12)	U
	5̶	3̶	¹4
−	1	7	8
	3	5	6

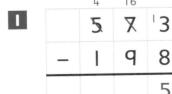

Now you try

1

	(4)	(16)	
	5̶	7̶	¹3
−	1	9	8
			5

2

	(6)	(14)	
	7̶	5̶	¹3
−	2	7	6
			7

3

		(4)	
	8	5̶	¹2
−	4	9	5

4

		(1)	
	8	2̶	5
−	3	7	7

5

	6	5̶	0
−	2	5	7

6

	4	8̶	6
−	1	9	8

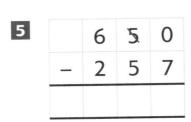

More practice

7
```
    4  7  5
 -  1  7  7
 _____
```

8
```
    5  3  3
 -  3  6  4
 _____
```

9
```
    6  2  4
 -  4  8  8
 _____
```

Set out these questions yourself to answer them.

10 475 – 186 = ?

11 714 – 447 = ?

12 730 – 187 = ?

Problem solving

13 How many more is 674 than 287?

14 At a concert there were 734 people. If 359 were children, how many were adults?

15 There are two parcels. One weighs 872g. The other is 475g lighter. How heavy is the lighter parcel?

16 Two numbers have a difference of 585. If the larger number is 912, what is the smaller number?

How did I find Step 8? ☐ Easy ☐ OK ☐ Difficult

Step 9: Four-digit subtraction exchanging twice, adjacent digits

For questions involving four-digit numbers, work from right to left in the same way. Here, you'll need to exchange a ten and a hundred or a hundred and a thousand. Just look carefully to see when a digit is larger than the one above it.

Th	H	T	U
	7	1	2	4
−		5	7	3

What to do

$7124 - 573 = ?$

1 Start with the units. $4 - 3 = 1$

2 Move to the tens. 7 is larger than 2 so exchange from the hundreds. Cross out the 1 and write one fewer above it. One fewer than 1 is 0. Take the hundred exchanged and write it in the tens column, so instead of 2 tens, you now have 10 tens + 2 tens = 12 tens. Then subtract. $12 - 7 = 5$

Th	H	T	U
		0		
7	1̸	¹2	4
−		5	7	3
			5	1

3 Then move to the hundreds. You can't take 5 away from 0 so exchange 1 thousand. Cross out the 7 thousands and write one fewer above it. One fewer than 7 is 6. Take the thousand and write it in the hundreds column, so instead of 0 hundreds you now have 10 hundreds + 0 hundreds = 10 hundreds. $10 - 5 = 5$

Th	H	T	U
6	10		
7̸	1̸	¹2	4
−	5	7	3
	5	5	1

4 Finally, look at the thousands column. There is nothing to subtract from the 6 thousands, so write 6 in the answer.

Th	H	T	U
6	10		
7̸	1̸	¹2	4
−	5	7	3
6	5	5	1

Now you try

1

	5	15	
5	6̸	6̸	¹0
−		4	8	5
				5

2

		4		
4	5̸	¹4	6
−	1	8	7	3
				3

3

	3		
9	4̸	¹8	8
−		9	9	7
				1

4

		4		
7	4	5̸	¹2
−	3	9	7

More practice

Set out these questions yourself to answer them.

5 8452 – 4356 = ?

Th   H   T   U

–

6 9506 – 7634 = ?

Th   H   T   U

–

Problem solving

A palindromic number is one that reads the same forwards and backwards.

Choose two digits with a difference of 2, for example 9 and 7.
Use them to create two four-digit palindromic numbers, for example 9779 and 7997.

Use the written method to find the difference between the two numbers. Here are some examples to try. Use the grid below for working.

7 9779 – 7997 = ?   _____   **8** 8668 – 6886 = ?   _____

9 7557 – 5775 = ?   _____   **10** 6446 – 4664 = ?   _____

What do you notice about the answers? _____

How did I find Step 9?   ☐ Easy   ☐ OK   ☐ Difficult

Step 10: Four-digit subtraction with a zero in the column to be exchanged from

When there is a zero in a column that you need to exchange from, you must move further left to the next column to exchange. Notice here that that are no tens in the top number and yet you need to exchange ten.

	Th	H	T	U
	6	8	0	2
−	1	3	4	5

What to do

$6802 - 1345 = ?$

1 Start with the units. 5 is larger than 2 so you need to exchange from the tens. There aren't any tens! So move left and exchange from the hundreds column first. Cross out the 8 and write one fewer above it. One fewer than 8 is 7. Take the hundred exchanged and write it in the tens column, so instead of 0 tens, you now have 10 tens.

	Th	H	T	U
			7	
	6	8	ⁱ0	2
−	1	3	4	5

2 Now go back to the units. 5 is larger than 2 so you need to exchange from the tens. Cross out the 10 and write one fewer. One fewer than 10 is 9. Write the ten exchanged as 10 units in the units column. Then subtract. $12 - 5 = 7$

	Th	H	T	U
			7	9
	6	8	0̸	ⁱ2
−	1	3	4	5
				7

3 Then work through the rest of the subtraction, moving from right to left. For the tens, $9 - 4 = 5$. For the hundreds, $7 - 3 = 4$. For the thousands, $6 - 1 = 5$.

	Th	H	T	U
			7	9
	6	8	0̸	ⁱ2
−	1	3	4	5
	5	4	5	7

Now you try

1

		5		
	5	6̸	ⁱ0	3
−	1	4	8	7

2

		4		
	4	5̸	ⁱ0	6
−	1	2	7	8

3

	9	8	0	4
−	2	3	9	7

4

	7	4	0	1
−	5	3	6	8

More practice

For these questions, the zero is in the hundreds column.

5
```
      8
   9 ¹0  4  8
 − 3  5  8  5
 _____
```

6
```
   5  0  5  9
 − 3  2  7  3
 _____
```

7
```
   9  0  3  6
 − 6  9  8  2
 _____
```

8
```
   6  0  2  8
 − 4  7  5  8
 _____
```

Problem solving

9 At a football match there were 7304 people. If 2178 were children, how many were adults?

10 A plane flew 7055km on Monday and 2684km on Tuesday. How much further did it fly on Monday than on Tuesday?

11 A large rabbit weighs 3036g. A smaller rabbit weighs 1864g less. How much does the smaller rabbit weigh?

12 How much larger than 2548 is the number 8804?

How did I find Step 10?   Easy   OK  Difficult

Check-up test 2 Three- and four-digit subtraction, with up to two exchanges and a zero

Step 6

1 7256 – 4324 = ?

```
    7 2 5 6
-   4 3 2 4
_____
```

2 6496 – 5843 = ?

Step 7

3 8173 – 4757 = ?

```
    8 1 7 3
-   4 7 5 7
_____
```

4 9390 – 3642 = ?

Step 8

5 475 – 287 = ?

```
    4 7 5
-   2 8 7
_____
```

6 715 – 457 = ?

Step 9

7 4439 – 2797 = ?

```
    4 4 3 9
-   2 7 9 7
_____
```

8 7452 – 367 = ?

Step 10

9 7602 – 1367 = ?

	7	6	0	2
–	1	3	6	7

10 9037 – 7882 = ?

☐ 9

☐ 10

Steps 6 to 10 mixed

Use the grid below for working.

11 How much smaller is 4747 than 5476?

_____ ☐ 11

12 A TV that cost £753 was reduced by £276 in a sale.
What is the sale price?

_____ ☐ 12

13 Subtract 6635 from 9407.

_____ ☐ 13

14 A plane travelled 8047km on Sunday and 2793km on
Monday. How much further did it travel on Sunday?

_____ ☐ 14

Total test score

Score	1	2	3	4	5	6	7	8	9	10	11	12	13	14
%	7	14	21	29	36	43	50	57	64	71	79	86	93	100

_____
14

Step 11: Five-digit subtraction exchanging twice, non-adjacent digits

Work in the same way for five-digit numbers, from right to left, exchanging if you need to.

What to do

$52814 - 39371 = ?$

	TTh	Th	H	T	U
			7		
	5	2	8̶	¹1	4
−	3	9	3	7	1
				4	3

1. Start with the units. $4 - 1 = 3$

2. Move left to the tens. Because you can't take 7 away from 1, you must exchange a hundred from the column to its left. Cross out the 8 hundreds and write one fewer above it. One fewer than 8 is 7. Think of a hundred as 10 tens and add it to the 1 ten already there to get 11 tens. $11 - 7 = 4$

3. Then move to the hundreds. $7 - 3 = 4$

			7		
	5	2	8̶	¹1	4
−	3	9	3	7	1
			4	4	3

4. Move to the thousands. Because you can't take 9 away from 2, you must exchange a ten thousand from the column to its left. Cross out the 5 ten thousands and write one fewer above it. One fewer than 5 is 4. You now have 12 thousands. $12 - 9 = 3$

	4		7		
	5̶	¹2	8̶	¹1	4
−	3	9	3	7	1
		3	4	4	3

5. Finally, look at the ten thousands column. $4 - 3 = 1$

	4		7		
	5̶	¹2	8̶	¹1	4
−	3	9	3	7	1
	1	3	4	4	3

Now you try

1

				6	
	5	2	8	7̶	¹4
−	2	4	3	2	7
					7

2

			4		
	8	4	5̶	¹5	9
−	7	8	3	8	4
					5

3

	9	8	2	3̶	3
−		4	7	1	8

4

	4	5	6	3	7
−	1	7	3	4	6

More practice Set out these questions yourself to answer them.

5 85 264 – 64 958 = ?

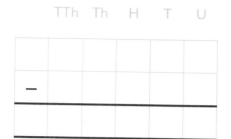

6 83 631 – 5327 = ?

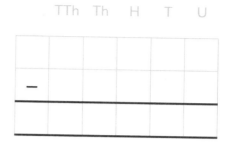

Problem solving

Choose two digits with a difference of 3, for example 9 and 6. Use them to create two five-digit palindromic numbers, with alternating digits, for example 96969 and 69696.

Find the differences between these numbers. Use the grid below for working.

7 96 969 – 69 696 = ? _____   **8** 85 858 – 58 585 = ? _____

9 74 747 – 47 474 = ? _____   **10** 63 636 – 36 363 = ? _____

What do you notice about the answers? _____

11 Choose two digits with a difference of 4
and explore patterns in the same way.
What do you notice? Use spare paper. _____

How did I find Step 11?   ☐ Easy   ☐ OK   ☐ Difficult

Step 12: Five-digit subtraction exchanging twice, adjacent digits

In Step 9, you subtracted four-digit numbers where you needed to exchange from two columns next to each other. Can you do the same with five-digit numbers?

TTh	Th	H	T	U
4	7	6	3	7
− 1	2	9	4	6

What to do

$47637 - 12946 = ?$

1 Start with the units. $7 - 6 = 1$

2 Move to the tens. 4 is larger than 3 so exchange from the hundreds. Cross out the 6 and write one fewer above it. One fewer than 6 is 5. Take the hundred exchanged and write it in the tens column, so instead of 3 tens you now have 10 tens + 3 tens = 13 tens. Then subtract. $13 - 4 = 9$

TTh	Th	H	T	U
		5		
4	7	6̶	¹3	7
− 1	2	9	4	6
			9	1

3 Then move to the hundreds. You can't take 9 away from 5 so exchange 1 thousand. Cross out the 7 thousands and write one fewer above it. One fewer than 7 is 6. Take the thousand and write it in the hundreds column, so instead of 5 hundreds you now have 10 hundreds + 5 hundreds = 15 hundreds. $15 - 9 = 6$

TTh	Th	H	T	U
	6	15		
4	7̶	6̶	¹3	7
− 1	2	9	4	6
		6	9	1

4 Finally, look at the thousands and then the ten thousands column and subtract. $6 - 2 = 4$ and $4 - 1 = 3$

TTh	Th	H	T	U
	6	15		
4	7̶	6̶	¹3	7
− 1	2	9	4	6
3	4	6	9	1

Now you try

1

		2		
8	8	6	3̶	¹0
− 4	3	3	4	6
				4

2

		5		
4	8	6̶	¹1	9
− 3	2	9	4	4
			7	5

3

9	5	4	6	9
− 5	7	8	3	3

4

6	4	4	3	7
−	2	7	6	2

More practice

5
```
    8 8 9 6 1
  − 6 7 8 6 3
  _____
```

6
```
    7 9 1 7 8
  −   6 7 9 3
  _____
```

Set out these questions yourself to answer them.

7 57 226 − 35 876 = ?

TTh	Th	H	T	U
−				

8 75 957 − 45 768 = ?

TTh	Th	H	T	U
−				

Problem solving

9 An athletics stadium has 76 245 seats. At an athletics meeting in the stadium, 55 475 people attended. How many empty seats were there?

10 68 753 people visited the Multiplex cinema in October. 7384 fewer than this visited in November. How many visited in November?

How did I find Step 12? ☐ Easy   ☐ OK   ☐ Difficult

Step 13: Five-digit subtraction with a zero in the column to be exchanged from

In Step 10, you were shown what to do with a zero in a column you needed to exchange from. These five-digit numbers have a zero in them.

$83702 - 12945 = ?$

TTh	Th	H	T	U
		6		
8	3	7̶	'0	2
– 1	2	9	4	5

What to do

1. Start with the units. 5 is larger than 2 so exchange from the tens. There aren't any tens! So move left and exchange from the hundreds. Cross out the 7 and write one fewer above it. One fewer than 7 is 6. Think of the hundred exchanged as 10 tens.

2. Now, go back to the units. 5 is larger than 2 so you need to exchange from the tens. Cross out the 10 and write one fewer above it. One fewer than 10 is 9. Write the ten as 10 units in the units column. Then subtract the units and the tens. $12 – 5 = 7$ and $9 – 4 = 5$

		6	9	
8	3	7̶	'0̶	'2
– 1	2	9	4	5
			5	7

3. Then work through the rest of the subtraction, moving from right to left. Watch out for any other exchanging needed. Here, as you can't take 9 hundreds from the 6 hundreds, exchange from the thousands. For the hundreds, $16 – 9 = 7$. For the thousands, $2 – 2 = 0$. For the ten thousands, $8 – 1 = 7$.

	2	16	9	
8	3̶	7̶	'0̶	'2
– 1	2	9	4	5
7	0	7	5	7

Now you try

1

		5		
7	3	6̶	'0	2
– 5	2	3	4	9

2

		4		
8	5̶	'0	3	7
– 2	2	3	7	5

3

6	3	3̶	0	3
– 5	2	7	2	8

4

7	2	6	0	5
– 3	6	3	7	9

More practice

5
```
    9 0 4 8 7
  - 4 6 8 6 5
  _____
```

6
```
    8 5 0 1 8
  - 3 7 3 7 4
  _____
```

7
```
    6 0 4 0 7
  - 5 6 3 7 9
  _____
```

8
```
    8 9 6 0 3
  -   7 5 8 4
  _____
```

Problem solving

9 A forestry service planted 50 364 trees last year but cut down 36 762 trees. How many more trees were planted than were cut down?

10 On a hillside in a nature reserve 37 674 butterflies were counted in June. In July, 41 056 were counted. How many more were counted in July than in June?

11 Find the difference between 40 694 and 27 751.

12 Gita, a bank clerk, earns £33 773 per year. Her boss earns £84 059. How much more does her boss earn than Gita?

How did I find Step 13?   ☐ Easy   ☐ OK   ☐ Difficult

Step 14: Five-digit subtraction exchanging three or four times

Now that you are confident in exchanging twice, you can easily exchange three or more times!

What to do

72642 – 39768 = ?

1 Start with the units. 8 is larger than 2 so exchange from the tens. 12 – 8 = 4

	TTh	Th	H	T	U
				5	13
	7	2	6	4	¹2
–	3	9	7	6	8
				7	4

2 Move to the tens. 6 is larger than 3 so exchange from the hundreds. 13 – 6 = 7

			1	15	13
	7	2̶	6̶	4̶	¹2
–	3	9	7	6	8
				8	7	4

3 Then move to the hundreds. 7 is larger than 5 so exchange from the thousands. 15 – 7 = 8

	6	11	15	13	
	7̶	2̶	6̶	4̶	¹2
–	3	9	7	6	8
			2	8	7	4

4 Move to the thousands. 9 is larger than 1 so exchange from the ten thousands. 11 – 9 = 2

	6	11	15	13	
	7̶	2̶	6̶	4̶	¹2
–	3	9	7	6	8
		3	2	8	7	4

5 Finally, look at the ten thousands and subtract. 6 – 3 = 3

Now you try

1

				2	
	7	9	6	3̶	¹0
–	4	8	7	4	8
					2

2

				5	
	7	1	5	6̶	¹4
–		6	9	4	7
				1	7

3

	9	5	4	6	1
–	5	7	8	7	8

4

	8	6	6	6	7
–	4	8	7	6	9

5

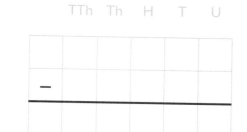

	5	5	4	5	3
−	2	8	0	9	5

6

	8	2	5	3	7
−	4	2	8	6	3

More practice   Set out these questions yourself to answer them.

7 57 251 − 35 876 = ?

TTh Th H T U

8 82 514 − 5768 = ?

TTh Th H T U

9 11 111 − 8888 = ?

TTh Th H T U

10 51 506 − 26 764 = ?

TTh Th H T U

Problem solving

11 A music arena has 55 377 seats.
At the concert on Saturday there
were 8489 empty seats. How many
seats were not empty?

12 Find the difference between each pair of numbers. Use spare paper for working.

a 55 555 and 7777 _____

b 44 444 and 6666 _____

c 33 333 and 5555 _____

d 22 222 and 4444 _____

How did I find Step 14?	☐ Easy	☐ OK	☐ Difficult

Step 15: Five-digit subtraction with zeros in the columns to be exchanged from

In Step 13, you saw what to do with a zero in a column you had to exchange from. These numbers have several zeros.

87002 − 12478 = ?

What to do						
		TTh	Th	H	T	U

What to do

1   Start with the units. 8 is larger than 2 so exchange from the tens. There aren't any tens! So move left and exchange from the hundreds. There aren't any hundreds! So move left and exchange from the thousands. Cross out the 7 and write 6 above. Think of the thousand exchanged as 10 hundreds.

		⁶			
	8	~~7~~	¹0	0	2
−	1	2	4	7	8

2   Now, exchange from the hundreds as there are 10 now. Cross out the 10 hundreds and write one fewer. One fewer than 10 is 9. Think of the hundred exchanged as 10 tens.

		⁶	⁹		
	8	~~7~~	~~0~~	¹0	2
−	1	2	4	7	8

3   Go back to the units. 8 is larger than 2 so exchange from the tens. Cross out the 10 tens and write one fewer. One fewer than 10 is 9. Write the ten as 10 units in the units column. Then subtract. 12 − 8 = 4

		⁶	⁹	⁹	
	8	~~7~~	~~0~~	~~0~~	¹2
−	1	2	4	7	8
					4

4   Work through the rest of the subtraction, moving from right to left. For the tens, 9 − 7 = 2. For the hundreds, 9 − 4 = 5. For the thousands, 6 − 2 = 4. For the ten thousands, 8 − 1 = 7.

		⁶	⁹	⁹	
	8	~~7~~	~~0~~	~~0~~	¹2
−	1	2	4	7	8
	7	4	5	2	4

Now you try

1

		⁸	⁹		
	8	9	~~0~~	¹0	2
−	7	2	3	4	9

2

		⁴	⁹		
	5	~~0~~	¹0	4	8
−	2	2	3	7	5

3

	7	3	0	0	3
−	5	2	7	2	8

4

	6	0	0	0	5
−	3	6	3	7	9

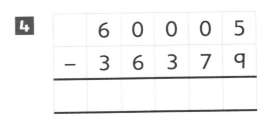

More practice

5
```
    9 0 0 3 7
  - 7 6 8 7 5
  _____
```

6
```
    8 5 0 0 8
  - 5 8 3 7 3
  _____
```

Problem solving

7 In one year 70 047 people visited a tourist attraction in London. If 35 486 of them were adults, how many were children?

8 Efia won £62 002 in the lottery. She gave £47 463 of it to charity. How much did she keep for herself?

9 Find the difference between 40 004 and 33 333.

10 A rescue centre helped a total of 32 008 dogs last year. They found 29 453 of them homes. How many didn't they find a home for?

11 Jan earned £30 006 last year. He paid £8536 in tax and spent the rest. How much did he spend?

How did I find Step 15? ☐ Easy ☐ OK ☐ Difficult

Check-up test 3 Five-digit subtraction, with several exchanges and zeros

Step 11

1 64 732 − 55 317 = ?

	6	4	7	3	2
−	5	5	3	1	7

2 60 638 − 17 587 = ?

Step 12

3 64 438 − 41 972 = ?

	6	4	4	3	8
−	4	1	9	7	2

4 75 954 − 33 257 = ?

Step 13

5 95 039 − 21 375 = ?

	9	5	0	3	9
−	2	1	3	7	5

6 60 403 − 28 329 = ?

Step 14

7 95 463 − 47 588 = ?

	9	5	4	6	3
−	4	7	5	8	8

8 85 151 − 29 075 = ?

Step 15

9 93 006 – 51 149 = ?

	9	3	0	0	6
–	5	1	1	4	9

10 90 007 – 36 379 = ?

–					

☐ 9
☐ 10

Steps 11 to 15 mixed

Use the grids below for working.

11 A rugby stadium has 58 382 seats. At the match on Saturday there were 18 649 empty seats. How many seats were occupied? _____

☐ 11

12 Find the difference between 52 694 and 27 751. _____

☐ 12

13 Simon, an IT manager, earns £33 673 per year. His boss earns £84 009. How much more than Simon does his boss earn? _____

☐ 13

14 Subtract 37 073 from 73 037. _____

☐ 14

Total test score

Score	1	2	3	4	5	6	7	8	9	10	11	12	13	14
%	7	14	21	29	36	43	50	57	64	71	79	86	93	100

☐ 14

Step 16: Large number subtraction

What to do

1 You've learnt how to do written subtraction for up to five-digit numbers. Subtracting even larger numbers is just as easy!

2 Just remember to exchange where needed.

HTh	TTh	Th	H	T	U
4	9		5	13	
5	0	6	6	4	1
− 2	4	8	2	7	3
2	5	8	3	6	8

Now you try

1 Seven hundred and nine thousand, three hundred and seventeen minus thirty-one thousand, four hundred and forty-six.

	7	0	9	3	1	7
−		3	1	4	4	6

2 Nine hundred and twenty thousand, three hundred and fifty subtract six hundred and eighty-two thousand and eighteen.

	9	2	0	3	5	0
−	6	8	2	0	1	8

3 Eight hundred thousand, five hundred and twelve minus two hundred and sixty thousand, two hundred and nineteen.

	8	0	0	5	1	2
−	2	6	0	2	1	9

4 Two hundred and sixty-one thousand nine hundred and three subtract ninety-four thousand, six hundred and seven.

	2	6	1	9	0	3
−		9	4	6	0	7

5 Six hundred and ninety thousand and thirty minus seventy-eight thousand, two hundred and forty-one.

	6	9	0	0	3	0
−		7	8	2	4	1

6 Five hundred and twelve thousand and forty-two subtract two hundred and six thousand and sixty-five.

	5	1	2	0	4	2
−	2	0	6	0	6	5

More practice

Set out these questions yourself to answer them.

7 Six hundred and twenty-six thousand, four hundred and three take away four hundred and eighty-six thousand, six hundred and nine.

HTh TTh Th H T U

—

8 Two hundred and fifty thousand and seventeen take away eighty-nine thousand, four hundred and eight.

HTh TTh Th H T U

—

Problem solving

9 A group of people raised £385 057 for two charities. They gave £184 488 to one charity. How much did they give to the other?

_____

10 There were 573 684 people at an Olympic event. If 375 427 of them were female, how many were male?

_____

11 Find the difference between two palindromic six-digit numbers that can be made with the digits 3 and 7, for example 737 737 subtract 377 773. Try different ways, working on the grid or using spare paper.

Can you find a question with the answer 435 644?

_____

How did I find Step 16? ☐ Easy ☐ OK ☐ Difficult

Step 17: Decimal subtraction two decimal places

Now that you can subtract whole numbers, subtracting decimals is almost as easy! All you need to do is to set out the digits in the correct columns and subtract in the same way!

$34.56 - 8.47 = ?$

H	T	U	.	t	h
			.	⁴	
	3	4	.	5̶	¹6
−		8	.	4	7
					9

What to do

1 Start with the right-hand column. Because you can't take 7 away from 6, you must exchange from the column to its left. Cross out the 5 tenths and write one fewer above it. One fewer than 5 is 4. Think of the tenth as 10 hundredths and add it to the 6 hundredths. $16 - 7 = 9$

2 Then move to the tenths. $4 - 4 = 0$

			.	⁴	
	3	4	.	5̶	¹6
−		8	.	4	7
			.	0	9

3 Continue working from right to left to complete the subtraction.

4 Remember to put the decimal point in your answer, in line with the decimal points above.

	²		.	⁴	
	3̶	⁴4	.	5̶	¹6
−		8	.	4	7
	2	6	.	0	9

Now you try

1 $519.74 - 43.27 = ?$

	5	1	9	.	7̶ ⁶	¹4
−		4	3	.	2	7
				.	4	7

2 $45.59 - 7.84 = ?$

		4	5	.	5 ⁴	9
−			7	.	8	4
						5

3 $352.74 - 127.83 = ?$

	3	5	2	.	7	4
−	1	2	7	.	8	3

4 $50.43 - 13.79 = ?$

		5	0	.	4	3
−		1	3	.	7	9

More practice

Set out these questions yourself to answer them.

5 852.64 – 649.58 = ?

6 836.31 – 53.27 = ?

Problem solving

7 Jo runs 56.72km in January and 64.18km in February. How much further does she run in February?

8 Jack wants to buy a laptop costing £746.45. He already has £673.83. How much more does he need to save?

9 Charlie weighed 90.48kg before a diet. After a diet his weight had fallen to 74.73kg. How much weight had he lost?

| How did I find Step 17? | ☐ Easy | ☐ OK | ☐ Difficult |

Step 18: Decimal subtraction different numbers of decimal places

What to do

In this last step, the questions have different numbers of decimal places so you must be careful to write the digits in the correct columns. Sometimes it can help to write zeros into the empty spaces. Don't forget to put the decimal point in your answer each time!

Now you try
Set out these questions yourself to answer them.

1 492.76 – 16.825 = ?

	H	T	U	.	t	h	th
	4	9	2	.	7	6 ⁵⁄₆	¹0
–							5
							5

2 205.7 – 52.139 = ?

	H	T	U	.	t	h	th
	2	0	5	.	7	0	0
–							

3 842.9 – 9.82 = ?

	H	T	U	.	t	h
	8	4	2	.	9	0
–						

4 78.135 – 38.66 = ?

	H	T	U	.	t	h	th
		7	8	.	1	3	5
–							

More practice
Set out these questions yourself to answer them.

5 900.8 – 174.631 = ?

	H	T	U	.	t	h	th
–							

6 801.3 – 562.49 = ?

	H	T	U	.	t	h
–						

Problem solving

Check your answers by adding.

7 Two large crates weigh 406.9kg and 384.73kg. How much heavier is one crate than the other?

8 A baby weighed 3.46kg at birth. At six months old he weighed 7.257kg. How much weight had he gained?

9 A river is 7.84m wide at its narrowest point and 204.9m wide at its widest point. How much wider is it at its widest point than at its narrowest point?

10 What is 30.08ml less than 125ml?

11 Ali took £278 spending money on holiday. On the first week of his holiday he spent £183.67. How much did he have left for the second week?

12 Usain Bolt ran 100m in 9.572 seconds. How much faster did he run than the 1891 world record holder who ran it in 10.8 seconds?

How did I find Step 18? ☐ Easy ☐ OK ☐ Difficult

Final test Subtraction of whole numbers and decimals

Steps 16 to 18

1 Nine hundred and twenty thousand, three hundred and fifty take away six hundred and eighty-two thousand and eighteen.

	9	2	0	3	5	0
−	6	8	2	0	1	8

2 Seven hundred and twenty thousand and seventeen take away four hundred and forty-six thousand, six hundred and two.

☐₁
☐₂

3 567.27 − 164.58 = ?

	5	6	7 .	2	7
−	1	6	4 .	5	8

4 828.36 − 55.29 = ?

☐₃
☐₄

5 742.9 − 16.826 = ?

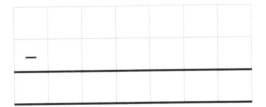

6 55.134 − 28.77 = ?

☐₅
☐₆

Use the grid below for working.

7 Subtract 90.92 from 902.9. _____

8 What is 42.15g less than 153g? _____

☐₇
☐₈

Steps 1 to 18 mixed

Use the grid below for working.

9 Two numbers have a difference of 733. If the larger
number is 961, what is the smaller number?   _____   ☐ 9

10 Monika had £6747 in a bank account. She took out £1824
to buy a car. How much money is left in the account?   _____   ☐ 10

11 Find the difference between 8338 and 3883.   _____   ☐ 11

12 How much larger is 45006 than 38574?   _____   ☐ 12

13 A puppy weighs 9036g. When it was born it weighed
5864g less. How much did it weigh when it was born?   _____   ☐ 13

14 A forestry service planted 50687 trees last year but cut
down 36779 trees. How many more trees were planted
than were cut down?   _____   ☐ 14

Total test score

Score	1	2	3	4	5	6	7	8	9	10	11	12	13	14
%	7	14	21	29	36	43	50	57	64	71	79	86	93	100

☐ 14

Schofield&Sims

the long-established educational publisher specialising in maths, English and science

Written Calculation comprises six **Pupil Books**, six **Answer Books**, a **Teacher's Guide** and a **Teacher's Resource Book** and uses methods recommended in the National Curriculum. Designed for use at Key Stage 2, each **Pupil Book** uses 18 carefully structured steps to guide the learner towards full mastery of each written method, supporting them in their national tests and other areas of the National Curriculum. **Written Calculation** also helps pupils develop confidence and fluency in their learning by practising and embedding place value, number facts and problem solving skills. The importance of estimating and checking answers is also emphasised.

Written Calculation: Subtraction leads pupils through the necessary steps for mastering the column method of subtraction. Pupils beginning this book should have an understanding of the value of digits in two- and three-digit numbers, experience of adding and subtracting single-digit numbers and know their subtraction number bonds to 20.

Each of the 18 steps features the following sections.
- *What to do* – detailed explanations and a worked example.
- *Now you try* – questions that are similar to those in the worked example.
- *More practice* – questions that are a little more difficult and provide less support than those in *Now you try*.
- *Problem solving* – word problems.
- *Self-evaluation rating* – to help identify pupils who may be struggling with the step.

Three *Check-up tests* and a *Final test* enable you to monitor pupils' progress and quickly convert scores to percentages. These scores may later be recorded on the *Group record sheet*.

The accompanying **Teacher's Guide** provides useful notes and ideas for planning lessons, enabling a whole-school approach. Detailed *Teaching notes* outline clear learning objectives and a *Summary of the steps* for each **Pupil Book** is included. Photocopiable *Assessment resources* allow you to monitor and assess pupils' progress.

Supplementary *Further practice* and *Problem solving questions* can be found in the **Teacher's Resource Book**. These photocopiable resources may be used for further practice, assessment, revision or homework and correspond to the steps covered in each of the **Pupil Books**.

The full range of books in the series is as follows.

Addition	978 07217 1266 6	**Addition Answers**	978 07217 1272 7
Subtraction	978 07217 1267 3	**Subtraction Answers**	978 07217 1273 4
Multiplication 1	978 07217 1268 0	**Multiplication 1 Answers**	978 07217 1274 1
Multiplication 2	978 07217 1269 7	**Multiplication 2 Answers**	978 07217 1275 8
Division 1	978 07217 1270 3	**Division 1 Answers**	978 07217 1276 5
Division 2	978 07217 1271 0	**Division 2 Answers**	978 07217 1277 2
Teacher's Guide	978 07217 1278 9	**Teacher's Resource Book**	978 07217 1300 7

Free downloads, available from the **Written Calculation** page of the Schofield & Sims website, enhance the effectiveness of the series. These are updated as necessary to ensure that **Schofield & Sims Written Calculation** meets the requirements of the National Curriculum.

ISBN 978-07217-1267-3

9 780721 712673

ISBN 978 07217 1267 3
Key Stage 2
Age range 7–11 years
£3.95
(Retail price)

For further information and to place your order visit
www.schofieldandsims.co.uk or telephone 01484 607080